Self-Love

A thirteen-week guide to exploring the fundamentals of self-compassion, common humanity, and mindfulness.

Ready to begin your journey?

Scan here.

INTRO	Journal Overview

If a close friend was going through a tough time, what would you do to help them? Most likely, you would empathize with them and treat them with kindness. The problem is that when it comes to ourselves, we develop harsh judgments and become overly critical.

Over the next 90 days, you will learn strategies that will help you rewire your brain and improve your overall well-being so you can be a kind friend to yourself, as well. The goal of this journal is to permanently change the way you treat and feel about yourself.

This journal was designed to improve your self-compassion through evidence-based techniques and therapeutic practices.

We know we should do many things for our physical well-being (like exercising and eating well), but too often, we neglect our mental well-being. This 90-day, science-based journal teaches you to form new thinking patterns that reshape your brain so you can experience positive and lasting change.

First hardcover edition October 2021

Journal design by Shelby Tessier (V28)

ISBN 978-1-7773737-0-2 (hardcover)

Published by Switch Research Inc.

www.switchresearch.org

Check *List*

Week 01	☐
DAY 01	☐
DAY 02	☐
DAY 03	☐
DAY 04	☐
DAY 05	☐
DAY 06	☐
DAY 07	☐

Week 02	☐
DAY 01	☐
DAY 02	☐
DAY 03	☐
DAY 04	☐
DAY 05	☐
DAY 06	☐
DAY 07	☐

Week 03	☐
DAY 01	☐
DAY 02	☐
DAY 03	☐
DAY 04	☐
DAY 05	☐
DAY 06	☐
DAY 07	☐

Week 04	☐
DAY 01	☐
DAY 02	☐
DAY 03	☐
DAY 04	☐
DAY 05	☐
DAY 06	☐
DAY 07	☐

Week 05	☐
DAY 01	☐
DAY 02	☐
DAY 03	☐
DAY 04	☐
DAY 05	☐
DAY 06	☐
DAY 07	☐

Week 06	☐
DAY 01	☐
DAY 02	☐
DAY 03	☐
DAY 04	☐
DAY 05	☐
DAY 06	☐
DAY 07	☐

Week 07	☐
DAY 01	☐
DAY 02	☐
DAY 03	☐
DAY 04	☐
DAY 05	☐
DAY 06	☐
DAY 07	☐

Week 08	☐
DAY 01	☐
DAY 02	☐
DAY 03	☐
DAY 04	☐
DAY 05	☐
DAY 06	☐
DAY 07	☐

Week 09	☐
DAY 01	☐
DAY 02	☐
DAY 03	☐
DAY 04	☐
DAY 05	☐
DAY 06	☐
DAY 07	☐

Week 10	☐
DAY 01	☐
DAY 02	☐
DAY 03	☐
DAY 04	☐
DAY 05	☐
DAY 06	☐
DAY 07	☐

Week 11	☐
DAY 01	☐
DAY 02	☐
DAY 03	☐
DAY 04	☐
DAY 05	☐
DAY 06	☐
DAY 07	☐

Week 12	☐
DAY 01	☐
DAY 02	☐
DAY 03	☐
DAY 04	☐
DAY 05	☐
DAY 06	☐
DAY 07	☐

Week 13	☐
DAY 01	☐
DAY 02	☐
DAY 03	☐
DAY 04	☐
DAY 05	☐
DAY 06	☐
DAY 07	☐

PART 01	PART 02	PART 03

Exploring the Fundamentals of Self-Compassion

You will explore self-kindness, common humanity, and mindfulness over the next three weeks. Each week you will have a chance to dive deeper into an aspect of self-compassion through strategic writing prompts and real-life applications.

WEEK 01
Self-Kindness

DAY 01

Self-Kindness

Self-kindness is at the core of being self-compassionate.[1] It means being gentle with yourself and acknowledging that you are doing your best rather than punishing yourself for imperfections or failures.

As your first step toward self-love, look for ways to be kind to yourself today. Begin by writing a phrase, a few sentences, or even a letter to yourself below. Tell yourself you care and are ready to begin being kind and gentle with yourself.

Daily Intention & Reflection

→ Each day of your self-love journey, you'll set a daily intention or complete a task. Today, set an intention to be self-kind. Come up with a thought or phrase you can reflect on throughout the day as a self-kindness reminder. For example, you might choose, *"In this moment, I am enough."* New to intention setting? Check out our intention setting guide in Appendix A (page 119) for more information.

DAY 02

Choosing Self-Kindness over Self-Judgment

Self-kindness can take many different forms. It may mean talking positively to ourselves or having loving feelings about ourselves. Here are some ways you can practice self-kindness:

Encourage kind thoughts

Are there small goals you have achieved that you can celebrate? Can you respect a tough decision you have made? Use the space below to celebrate your strengths.

Embrace kind feelings

Can you forgive yourself for a past mistake? Can you show yourself understanding for an expectation you didn't meet? Remind yourself, *"I am enough; I am worthy; I deserve to be happy."*

Daily Intention & Reflection

→ Embrace kind feelings toward yourself in this moment. Reflect on ways you can be kind to yourself and think about your answers to the questions on this page.

→ Set another intention to be self-kind today. This may feel odd or uncomfortable to start, but it is normal to feel that way. The more you practice, the more natural it will feel.

DAY 03 | Being Self-Kind, Not Self-Judging

Self-kindness doesn't always come naturally. Sometimes, we think the only way we can succeed is to be self-critical.

We often feel anger or resentment toward ourselves when we fall short of our ideals. In reality, harsh self-criticism increases stress, resentment, and frustration, which reduces our ability to cope and take future action.[2]

Daily Intention & Reflection

→ Think of a recent situation when you were self-critical and viewed yourself with harsh judgment. Reflect on how it made you feel.

→ Now think of a time when a friend told you about a painful or challenging experience. How did you respond to your friend? How would you have responded to yourself if you were going through the same experience? What kinder response could you tell yourself when you experience something painful or challenging over the next week?

DAY 04

Self-Kindness Meditation

Self-kindness means acknowledging your emotional needs and taking care of them.[3] Emotional needs are feelings or conditions that need to be met for us to feel at peace.

For example, we all need to feel appreciated, loved, safe, and part of a community. When our emotional needs are not met, we may feel uneasy, dissatisfied, or sad.

Daily Intention & Reflection

→ Can you identify a time when you felt an emotional need was not met? Why is this emotional need important to you?

→ How can you communicate and resolve not having your emotional needs met, and how can this help you? Allow this emotional need to inspire your intention today. When you have your intention, try meditating on this. If you're new to meditation and looking for tips and guidance on how to get started, please refer to our meditation guide in Appendix B (page 120).

Reframing Self-Judgment into Self-Kindness

When we fall short of our expectations, we can approach the situation with self-kindness or self-judgment.[4] It can be easy to get down on ourselves when we realize that we have been self-critical; however, we can work to identify when this happens and consciously reframe the self-judgment into self-kindness.

Quick steps to reframing self-judgment[5]

01. Identify when you are making a harsh judgment about yourself.

02. Ask yourself: *"Is this judgment completely true? Am I being overly harsh?"*

03. Think of an alternative response that is self-kind.

04. Remember this response if you find yourself making harsh self-judgments in the future.

Daily Intention & Reflection

→ Reflect on a situation when you were unusually hard on yourself or a recent instance when you were self-critical. What was your initial self-critical thought? Is this judgment completely true? What are some alternative self-kind responses? Why are these new responses better? For more information and guidance on reframing, explore our guide in Appendix C (page 121).

Harsh self-judgment	Self-kind response
I am a horrible cook.	I often get compliments on my favorite dish.

DAY 06 | Self-Kindness and Self-Care

Part of self-kindness means practicing self-care. Self-care is a great way to honor yourself with an action you are doing simply for your own enjoyment. What self-care activities do you do to show yourself kindness?

Examples of self-care

Taking some quiet personal time, getting enough sleep, taking a bath, treating yourself to a good coffee, getting outdoors, going for a walk, or talking with a friend about how you are feeling.

Daily Intention & Reflection

→ Think about what self-care activities you can incorporate into your day-to-day life to show yourself kindness. Write a list of activities you can do to honor your self-worth. If you like to plan, write these activities into your weekly schedule as a reminder. If not, try writing a sticky note to remind yourself, or try setting a phone alarm.

DAY 07 | Write a Letter to Yourself

During this first week, you've worked through what it means to be self-kind. Take some time to reflect on the new ways you have learned to live a self-compassionate lifestyle.

Daily Intention & Reflection

→ Write a letter to yourself. What are you working through right now? How is your journey progressing so far? If you respond with a negative, self-critical thought, how can you reframe that to become self-kind? Remember to celebrate your progress as you continue to develop.

WEEK 02
Common Humanity

DAY 08

Common Humanity

Common humanity is the second core aspect of self-compassion.[6] Common humanity means you're not alone in your experiences. Acknowledging a common or shared humanity is recognizing that suffering, pain, and imperfection are all part of the human condition.

You may feel like you're the only one who makes mistakes, but this feeling of isolation prevents you from accepting your imperfections. Once you begin to accept the inevitability of imperfection that comes with being human, you will begin to realize that you deserve self-compassion.

Daily Intention & Reflection

→ Take some time to think about what common humanity means to you. Reflect on what the "inevitability of imperfection" means and why it is important to be self-compassionate.

DAY 09

The Shared Experience of Imperfection

Nobody's perfect. It's one of the fundamental laws of human existence. Find a quiet space and reflect on the following: *"If nobody is perfect, why do I feel like I need to be?"*

Daily Intention & Reflection

→ In what areas do you feel you need to be perfect? Why do you think this is? Do you expect perfection from others? If not, why do you expect it from yourself?

DAY 10

Embracing Common Humanity

According to self-compassion experts, feeling isolated and feeling a sense of common humanity are opposing forces.[7]

When we feel isolated, we feel like we're the only ones who make mistakes. This feeling can cause us to magnify the shame, guilt, or inadequacy we feel.

Daily Intention & Reflection

→ Is there something you've done recently that made you feel a sense of shame, guilt, or inadequacy? Are there times in your life when you felt you were the only one who has messed up? Reflect on how viewing things through the lens of a common humanity might change how you feel about yourself.

DAY 11

The Fundamental Attribution Error

When something doesn't go your way, do you tend to view it as a personal failing or a result of something external? Many of us tend to see certain issues as personal failures, and we underestimate the impact of external factors. This tendency is known as the fundamental attribution error.[8]

For example, when you see someone act out at the cashier while waiting in line, you might assume they are an impatient person rather than someone who might be having a bad day because they were recently let go from their job.

Daily Intention & Reflection

→ When you make a mistake, do you assume it's because of a personal failing? How could remembering our common humanity help you consider the situation's external factors and help you be more self-compassionate?

DAY 12 | Being Comfortable in Your Imperfections

"I am perfect in my imperfections, secure in my insecurities, happy with my choices, strong in times of weakness, and beautiful in my own way. I am myself."

ANONYMOUS

Daily Intention & Reflection

→ Being self-kind means not seeing our imperfections as failures, but instead, as part of being human. What do you feel imperfect, insecure, or inadequate about? What is your typical reaction to these feelings? Are you hard on yourself? Reflect on how a sense of common humanity can comfort you and let you know that you are not alone in these feelings.

DAY 13 | Common Feelings

You have hopes and dreams. Do you suppose others do too? You feel loved and happy. Do you suppose others do too?

You feel inadequate or unworthy at times. Do you suppose others do too? You feel bullied or criticized. Do you suppose others do too?

Daily Intention & Reflection

→ Create a list of thoughts and feelings you hold about yourself. Do you suppose others have these thoughts and feelings, too? Reflect on ways that others might have similar thoughts or feelings. Feeling connected to others can help you develop a deeper sense of shared humanity.

DAY 14

Common Humanity Reflection

During the past week, we've focused on common humanity. What does common humanity mean to you? How has your need to be perfect changed?

Daily Intention & Reflection

→ Consider how you felt about your imperfections last week and how you feel about them now. You may still have insecurities; however, focus on growth and progress in your journey toward self-love. How have you begun to embrace your imperfections?

Mindfulness

DAY 15

What Does It Mean to Be Mindful?

Mindfulness is the third core aspect of self-compassion.[9] Mindfulness is attending to one's present moment with purpose and kindness. Mindfulness involves acknowledging your goals for personal growth, being present in moment-to-moment experiences, and approaching these ideas with an open heart and mind.[10,11]

By being mindful, you consider the current moment and your intentions for the future without judgment, simply acknowledging where you are in this exact time.

Daily Intention & Reflection

→ Consider how goals for personal growth and being present in moment-to-moment experiences work together.

DAY 16 | Your Purpose for Mindfulness

Exploring mindfulness and thinking about your values can help guide you in leading a life full of purpose. Take a moment to write down three core values or personal qualities that are important to you.

Values are different from goals and are not achieved like goals. Values are deep-rooted and serve as a guide throughout your lifetime. Some examples of values might be friendship, personal development, or adventure.

Daily Intention & Reflection

→ Based on your core values, set an intention for your mindfulness practice. Your intention should reflect your personal vision for growth. This intention may change or evolve throughout your practice. Remember to check our guide to intention setting in Appendix A (page 119) for more help and support.

DAY 17

What Is Your Story?

"The best way to capture the moment is to pay attention. This is how we cultivate mindfulness."

JON KABAT-ZINN

In mindfulness, it is important to be aware of both your internal and external experiences.[10] One way to do this is to record moments in a journal like this one. Capturing moments of your life through journaling can feel as though you are writing your own story, giving you a mindful presence in your journey.

Daily Intention & Reflection

→ Consider your five senses: touch, taste, smell, sight, and sound. Which senses are you most aware of in this moment? Describe how this mindfulness practice made you feel. For example, did it ground you in the here and now? Did it bring your attention to anything you don't usually notice?

The Attitude of an Open Heart

"Mindfulness is a way of befriending ourselves and our experience."

JON KABAT-ZINN

When you pay attention to your moment-to-moment experiences, how do you deal with them? Do you deal with those moments without thought or feeling or with an attitude of disappointment or anger? How one deals with the present moment is an essential component of the mindfulness practice.[10]

Mindfulness is dealing with each moment with an attitude of compassion, gratitude, and acceptance, as well as an open heart and open mind. Consider a current struggle or challenge in your life that is causing you stress. Write down how this experience makes you feel.

Write about these feelings freely and without revision. Take a moment to reflect on what you wrote. As you reflect on these feelings, place your hand on your chest, take a few slow and purposeful breaths, and tell yourself, *"This is struggling."*

Now that you're mindful of your experience, try to access the most deeply compassionate part of yourself and then write a response to yourself. How might you respond to yourself with kindness and without judgment?

Daily Intention & Reflection

→   Set an intention to revisit this exercise once this week when you are struggling or feeling stress.

DAY 19

Finding Another Meaning Through Mindfulness

When going through a challenging experience, one may become so immersed in their immediate emotional response that it is difficult to consider an alternative perspective of the experience.[9]

Think about a recent or present challenging experience. How did you first react to that situation? Take a moment to reflect on different perspectives of this experience. Is there something you could learn from this experience? Can you find a silver lining (a hopeful prospect in a difficult situation)?

Daily Intention & Reflection

→ Set an intention to find a new perspective on the meaning of one challenging experience this week.

DAY 20 | Mindfulness Meditation

Think of an intention for your mindfulness practice. Find a quiet place to sit and meditate on your intention.

During your meditation, bring awareness to your present moment and view it through the lens of acceptance.

Daily Intention & Reflection

→ Jot down any thoughts you had during your mindfulness practice.

DAY 21 | Reflect on Mindfulness

This week you have explored mindfulness. Reflect on what you've learned about yourself through mindfulness.

Daily Intention & Reflection

→ How has the practice of mindfulness helped you? How has your intention for mindfulness changed or evolved? What aspects of mindfulness have you begun to incorporate into your day-to-day life?

PART 01	PART 02	PART 03

Expanding Your Self-Compassion

You've begun your journey by focusing on self-kindness, common humanity, and mindfulness. Next, you will have the opportunity to focus on related practices such as: self-acceptance, self-reflection, and gratitude.

WEEK 04
Self-Acceptance

DAY 22

Self-Acceptance

Self-acceptance describes a relationship we can have with ourselves. This relationship is characterized by an unconditional acceptance of our strengths and weaknesses.[12]

We often celebrate our achievements; however, accepting ourselves at our lowest with all our faults and flaws is a mark of unconditional self-acceptance. Self-acceptance allows you to see and love yourself for who you are.

Daily Intention & Reflection

→ Do you love yourself for who you are? Are there things about yourself you don't easily accept? Reflect on the things you don't fully accept about yourself. Write about the things you love about yourself and notice how your feelings change.

DAY 23

You Are Fundamentally Worthy of Love

How can someone accept their flaws and still love themselves? Put simply, they view themselves as they view all of humanity— as being fundamentally worthy of esteem and love. Individuals who are self-accepting know deep down that they are "enough" and that no mistake can negate their fundamental worth as a person who is worthy of love.

Becoming self-accepting can be difficult because it brings attention to our mistakes and flaws. The more you can recognize your fundamental worth, the easier it will be to develop your self-acceptance.

Daily Intention & Reflection

→ Reflect on how you can view everyone as being fundamentally worthy of love. Reflect on the idea that you are fundamentally worthy of love. An example of this could be, *"I'm not perfect, but I'm still worthy of love."*

DAY 24 — A Self-Acceptance Affirmation

Self-acceptance can be difficult. Everyone has at least one thing they dislike about themselves, or one aspect of themselves they wish were different.

However, it is important that we acknowledge and accept these things to prevent them from building up, causing us to dislike ourselves. Some things we may be able to change. Some we may not, and that's okay.

Daily Intention & Reflection

→ Using the table on the next page, write a list of things you haven't yet accepted about yourself. Read each of these statements to yourself. After each statement, affirm to yourself, *"I am enough. This does not define me. It is okay to be [insert the thing you do not accept here]. I am still worthy of love."*

→ In the space below, describe how writing down affirmations changes how you feel.

Example	Affirmation
I don't have my dream job.	I am enough. My job does not define me. It is okay to be in my current position at work. I am still worthy of love.

DAY 25

A Simple Self-Acceptance Reflection

What kind of relationship do you have with yourself? Is it one of unconditional self-acceptance?

Daily Intention & Reflection

→ Reflect on the things you need to accept about yourself. While reflecting, remember that your mistakes and imperfections do not make you any less worthy of love. For example, a statement of self-acceptance may be, *"In this moment, I am enough."*

Separating the Act From the Individual

There are no bad people; only bad actions. There are no selfish people; only selfish thoughts or acts. When we begin to separate the act from the individual, we begin to see our fundamental worth beneath our mistakes or misjudgments.[13]

If the flaw is in your thoughts or actions, then you can change it. In this way, you can identify personal weaknesses without letting them define you. Think back to some of the mistakes you've made. Do you say to yourself, *"I am a bad person"*? Or do you say, *"I am a person who made a mistake"*?

Daily Intention & Reflection

→ Write a response based on a recent mistake you have made. What would you say to yourself in the face of this mistake to affirm your fundamental worth?

DAY 27

Self-Acceptance and Self-Improvement

No amount of self-improvement can make up for a lack of self-acceptance. It is natural to strive to be the best version of ourselves, but we often mask a lack of self-acceptance through self-improvement.

Self-improvement with self-acceptance will most often bring satisfaction. Self-improvement without self-acceptance will not often satisfy you.[14] Are you trying to improve yourself with or without a sense of self-acceptance?

Daily Intention & Reflection

→ Using the table on the next page, write down an example of a self-improving statement without self-acceptance followed by an example of a self-improving statement with self-acceptance.

→ In the space below, reflect on how adding self-acceptance to these statements changes the way you feel.

Without self-acceptance	With self-acceptance
I will practice these healthy habits because I am unhappy with the way I look.	I love my body, and I will support it through healthy habits.

DAY 28 | Self-Acceptance and Self-Compassion

Self-acceptance means being kind to yourself despite your imperfections and being mindful of how you view and treat yourself.

Self-acceptance is one important way to show yourself compassion. No other human has more or less value than you do.

Daily Intention & Reflection

→ Reflect on your past week. What are some things you are doing to be more accepting of yourself? What parts of yourself could you be more accepting of? How does understanding that you are fundamentally worthy of love change how you view and treat yourself?

WEEK 05

Gratitude

| DAY 29 | Common Acts of Kindness |

We are not alone in our thoughts, feelings, or actions. Acknowledging others' kindness can strengthen our connection, not only with those closest to us but also with humanity in general.[15]

Daily Intention & Reflection

→ Write about something kind that someone did for you this week. What was this act of kindness? How did it make you feel about yourself? How did it make you feel about the person? How did it make you feel about humanity?

DAY 30

What Is Gratitude?

Gratitude is a deep feeling of appreciation for the good in our lives.[16] When we feel gratitude, we appreciate the gifts in our day-to-day lives, and we value our relationships with others.[17]

Feeling gratitude is an important part of self-compassion. Acknowledging the positive in our lives makes it easier to acknowledge the positive in ourselves.

Daily Intention & Reflection

→ What are you grateful for? Use the table on the next page to write down 10 things you are grateful for today. For example, these could be a person, a feeling, an object, or anything else you feel appreciation for.

→ How might you incorporate your gratitude for these things into your everyday life?

Things I am grateful for	
01	02
03	04
05	06
07	08
09	10

DAY 31

Finding Gratitude

Being mindful of your surroundings can help you appreciate the positive qualities in your life. However, we are not always aware of our surroundings.

Bringing your attention to unnoticed things can remind you of all the good that surrounds you. Look around your house or go outside, and write down three things you are grateful for that you might otherwise have taken for granted.

Daily Intention & Reflection

→ Why are you grateful for these things? What do you appreciate about these things that you wouldn't normally pay attention to?

DAY 32

Who Are You Grateful For?

Gratitude helps us appreciate the gifts we are given while also encouraging us to repay them. These gifts are not always tangible.[17] A gift may simply be acknowledging your appreciation for the good someone has brought into your life.

Reciprocating gifts helps to improve our relationships with others, which can, in turn, improve our relationship with ourselves. Write a short appreciation letter to someone who had a positive impact on your life, big or small.

Daily Intention & Reflection

→ Set an intention to show someone your gratitude and notice how it makes you feel.

DAY 33

Finding the Silver Lining

Having gratitude for the challenges in life can be difficult. It's not easy to be grateful during the hard times. Finding the silver lining in trying situations can help us be more accepting of the challenges we face.

When we are able to accept challenges, these situations may reveal themselves to be opportunities for self-growth.[18]

Daily Intention & Reflection

→ Reflect on a hard or challenging experience. Now, write down all the good things that wouldn't have happened to you without this experience. Did you learn something from it? Did you meet someone unexpected? Next time you experience a challenging situation, try to find one positive aspect of the situation.

DAY 34

Gratitude Meditation

Nature provides us with some of the most serene sights. Whether it be breathtaking mountainscapes, endless shorelines, lush forests, or the changing of the seasons, nature has a relaxing and calming effect. Meditating on the beauty of nature can help ground you during a busy day. It can help you to be mindful of your connection to the planet and to all life.

Find a calm place and meditate on the oneness and connection that nature brings you. Try to visualize a place in nature where you've felt at peace. What sounds did you hear? What aromas did you smell? Reflect on the gratitude you have for that time and place.

Daily Intention & Reflection

→ Jot down anything that came to you or that you learned from your meditation.

DAY 35

Reflecting on Gratitude

Gratitude is taking notice of and appreciating the positives in all aspects of life. Feeling gratitude can help you to be mindful of what your circumstances have afforded you. When we appreciate what and who we have, we can appreciate ourselves.

Daily Intention & Reflection

→ Reflect on this past week. What did you learn from exploring gratitude? What are you grateful for? How can you share your gratitude? How does your new understanding of gratitude change how you interact with your physical and social surroundings?

WEEK 06
Self-Compassion Myths

DAY 36

Myth 01 - Self-Compassion Is a Form of Self-Pity

One of the biggest myths about self-compassion is that it means feeling sorry for yourself.[19] Self-pity takes a *"woe is me"* approach that causes you to dwell on the negative things around you.

Self-compassion takes a kinder approach, common humanity helps you realize you're not alone in this, and mindfulness helps you to focus on the positive. Having a self-compassionate mindset means avoiding the *"woe is me"* perspective that self-pity endorses. What in your life right now are you feeling self-pity about?

Daily Intention & Reflection

→ Reflect on how you can start endorsing a self-compassionate mindset. An example might be rephrasing, *"I am a horrible cook!"* to *"I've recently started to cook, and I'm really improving!"*

DAY 37

Myth 02 - Self-Compassion Means Weakness

Many of us have faced difficult situations in which we've felt we needed to put on a brave face. Many assume that by showing emotion and letting your guard down, you are somehow showing signs of weakness.

However, research suggests that taking a self-compassionate approach improves coping and resilience.[20,21] Have you ever been in a situation in which you felt like you needed to put on a brave face and hide your emotions?

Daily Intention & Reflection

→   Reflect on how self-compassion can be your ally in difficult situations.

DAY 38

Myth 03 - Self-Compassion Will Make Me Complacent

People sometimes tell themselves, *"If I don't criticize myself for not living up to my standards, I'll become complacent; I'll accept mediocrity and stop trying to better myself."*

Judging ourselves with self-criticism creates negative emotions that lower our motivation. In contrast, self-compassion motivates accountability and positive change.[22]

Daily Intention & Reflection

→ Think of one area in which you can reduce self-criticism. Replace the negative perspective of self-criticism with the positive perspective of self-compassion.

DAY 39

Myth 04 - Self-Compassion Is Selfish

Many accuse themselves of being selfish when they are self-compassionate. We think, *"If I take time for myself, then I'm not fulfilling my duties to other people."* In this way, taking time for ourselves is viewed as a selfish act. We could do a hundred things for others but still feel undeserving of doing one thing for ourselves.

When you're busy, how do you typically treat yourself? When you are constantly pulled in different directions by others, do you take time for yourself, or do you feel guilty putting your own needs first?

Daily Intention & Reflection

→ Reflect on why taking time for yourself is a selfless act and what benefits it can bring to you and those around you.

DAY 40

Myth 05 - I Am Not Worthy of Self-Compassion

Some people feel that they must earn the right to be self-compassionate. Fortunately, common humanity tells us this: You are fundamentally worthy of love.

There is no action you can take to deserve self-compassion, because you inherently deserve it. This also implies that there is nothing you can do to make yourself unworthy of receiving self-compassion.

Daily Intention & Reflection

→ Using the table on the next page, write down four reasons why you are worthy of self-compassion.

→ In the space below, consider how can you demonstrate these reasons to yourself? (e.g., allowing yourself to rest, showing yourself patience).

Reasons I am worthy of self-compassion
01
02
03
04

DAY 41

Myth 6 - Mindfulness Means Not Planning Ahead

"It is good to have an end to journey toward, but it is the journey that matters in the end."

ERNEST HEMINGWAY

Mindfulness helps you focus on the present moment as a means of preventing or limiting your anxieties about the future. Being present does not mean you can't have future goals and dreams.

It means being aware of your present while not worrying about the past or being anxious about the future. You only have control over the present moment, and living in the present is how you can become more grounded.

Daily Intention & Reflection

→   What is one scenario in your life in which you could be more present?

DAY 42

Myth 7 - Mindfulness Makes You Turn Inward and Become Isolated

Mindfulness is an inward practice that helps us to draw focus to the present.

Mindfulness is a solo endeavor that grounds you in the present, allowing you to have more meaningful interactions. This strengthens your connections with others.

Daily Intention & Reflection

→ What is one relationship in your life that could be improved through mindfulness?

WEEK 07

Patience &
Self-Forgiveness

DAY 43

Patience

Patience is the capacity to accept delay, problems, or suffering without becoming annoyed or anxious.[23]

We can recognize when we're feeling impatient by focusing on our body. We might feel our pulse quicken, our breath may become shallow, or we may notice feelings of irritability or tension.

Impatience hinders self-compassion by causing us to focus on the delay, the problems, or the suffering. Would you consider yourself a patient person?

How patient are you with yourself when you're making personal changes? Are you patient with yourself when you make a mistake?

Daily Intention & Reflection

→ Reflect on how self-kindness, common humanity, and mindfulness can help you become more patient.

DAY 44

Patience and Self-Kindness

Making personal changes doesn't happen overnight. Changing how you treat and talk to yourself requires patience.

Daily Intention & Reflection

→ In the space below, reflect on how practicing more patience might change the way you talk to yourself.

→ Using the table on the next page, write down three things you want to change in your life. Then think of three ways in which you can practice patience during the progression of these goals.

Things I want to change in my life
01
02
03

Ways I can practice patience
01
02
03

DAY 45

Patience and Common Humanity

Practicing patience with others can help us understand how to be patient with ourselves. We've previously mentioned that common humanity helps us connect with others.

Understanding others' worth helps us to understand our own worth. Do you become easily impatient with certain people? Try separating the person from the situation when you feel impatient.

Daily Intention & Reflection

→ What if you viewed the person as being fundamentally worthy of love? Does this help you to be more patient with that person?

DAY 46

Mindfulness to Manage Feelings of Impatience

The feeling of impatience comes with distinct physical reactions. While situations can often be out of your control, how you interpret and manage your feelings is within your control. Mindful breathing can help manage these feelings.[24]

In these situations, the first step is to acknowledge that you're beginning to feel impatient. Acknowledge that your feelings are caused by an impatient reaction to a person or situation. Take a few deep meditative breaths using the 3 by 3 rule. If you would like to review this technique, refer to the meditation guide in Appendix B (page 120).

Focusing on your breathing draws attention away from the negative feelings associated with impatience. The more you can bring your attention to your breath, the less physically impatient you will feel.

Think of a situation in which you would normally feel impatient. Close your eyes and imagine yourself in the situation. What is happening? What sensations are you feeling? Once you start feeling impatient, practice meditative breathing. What happened? Did focusing on your breathing reduce your negative physical sensations?

Daily Intention & Reflection

→   Set an intention to practice mindful breathing the next time you start to feel impatient.

DAY 47

Self-Forgiveness

Forgiveness is a deliberate decision to let go of feelings of anger, resentment, and retribution. Sometimes it's hard to let go of our past mistakes.

Self-forgiveness is a challenging task for many of us. We may find it easier to forgive others than to forgive ourselves.

Daily Intention & Reflection

→   Reflect on why it is often harder to forgive yourself than it is to forgive others.

DAY 48

The 4 R's of Self-Forgiveness

Self-forgiveness means accepting your behavior. You may not condone it, but you can accept what has happened and be willing to move past it without ruminating on it. The 4 R's provide a simple way to remember how to forgive yourself.[25]

Responsibility

Taking responsibility for what has happened is the first step to being able to put it behind you. This means not making excuses or trying to justify your behavior.

Restoration

Taking actions to rectify your mistakes can help you take ownership and move past any guilt or shame.

Remorse

Feeling remorse helps lead to positive change. Shame, however, is a negative emotion that keeps you stuck in the past.

Renewal

Learning from your experience leads to personal growth and well-being. This learning process helps prevent the repetition of negative past events.

Daily Intention & Reflection

→ Is there anything you haven't forgiven yourself for? Maybe you haven't fully let go of shame or guilt? Use the 4 R's in the table on the next page to help you process anything you haven't fully forgiven yourself for.

I need to take responsibility for

I'm feeling

Actions I can take to rectify my mistakes

I learned

DAY 49

Practicing Self-Forgiveness

"There is no sense in punishing your future for the mistakes of your past. Forgive yourself, grow from it, and then let it go."

MELANIE KOULOURIS

Daily Intention & Reflection

→ Reflect on how patience and self-forgiveness can help you lead a self-compassionate life.

WEEK 08
Attitudes Toward Challenges

DAY 50

Introduction to a Growth Mindset

How we view challenges in our lives is an important part of self-compassion. Some challenges we encounter are painful, and this can make it easy to give up on ourselves.

However, when we embrace challenges as opportunities for growth, it is easier to overcome these obstacles and find a deeper meaning.[26]

Daily Intention & Reflection

→ Reflect on a difficult situation you have been avoiding. How does this situation make you feel? Why do you think you have been avoiding it? How can you view it as an opportunity to grow?

DAY 51

Acknowledging the Small Wins

You can't train to run a marathon in a day. It is the months of shorter runs before the marathon that help you to succeed. When you set a goal, it is easy to focus on the long-term outcome.

However, if you only consider the long-term outcome, you risk forgetting about what you need to do in the present to achieve your goal. Reflect on a time when you received the outcome that you wanted. Think about the small decisions you made each day to achieve your goal.

Daily Intention & Reflection

→ Is there a long-term project you've been working on? Set an intention to focus on the small wins this week. An example of this could be: *"My goal is to write a book. This week, I am celebrating writing 50 pages. I am confident that next week I can get to 75 pages."*

DAY 52 — Failure as an Opportunity for Growth

When we encounter a hard or painful situation, our first instinct is often to avoid the situation and ignore how it makes us feel. If we avoid these situations and don't take the time to reflect on them, we lose an opportunity to learn from them.[27]

Daily Intention & Reflection

→ Reflect on a difficult situation or a time when you felt you failed. Remember to be kind to yourself. Knowing what you know now, what would you do differently if faced with a similar situation?

DAY 53

Seeing Others as a Source of Inspiration

Comparing yourself to others can make it hard to adopt an attitude of growth. When we feel others have easily succeeded at things that have challenged us, this can make our own aspirations seem impossible.

When we compare ourselves to others, we criticize ourselves and dwell on what we don't have and where we fall short. However, instead of making direct comparisons, common humanity tells us to view others with humility, acknowledging their worth and valuing their strengths.

Daily Intention & Reflection

→ Think about someone you often compare yourself to. Write down the strengths you admire in this person. What does this person do that makes you look up to them? How can this person serve as a source of inspiration to you?

DAY 54

Choosing the Easy Way Versus the Fulfilling Way – Part 01

We often choose to do things to protect our ego.[28] We choose to do things that we know come easily rather than things that are challenging but ultimately more fulfilling. This choice stems from our inherent fear of failure.

Daily Intention & Reflection

→ Consider a recent decision that you struggled with. Below, reflect on what made it a difficult decision to make.

→ Using the table on the next page, reflect on the disadvantages of taking the easy way and the advantages of taking the fulfilling way.

Disadvantages of taking the easy way	Advantages of taking the fulfilling way

DAY 55

Choosing the Easy Way Versus the Fulfilling Way – Part 02

The fear of failure can motivate us to choose the easy path over a more challenging path. Some people view the risk of failure negatively and exaggerate the possible negative outcomes associated with failure.[29]

Rather than focus on positive outcomes, they tend to focus on the worst and unlikely outcomes. This is known as catastrophizing. Trying new things can be intimidating.

Daily Intention & Reflection

→ In the space below, reflect on a new skill or habit you have considered taking up, such as learning to play an instrument or starting a new exercise routine.

→ Reflect on what you think is the worst thing that could happen if you fail at this new skill or habit. How likely is this to actually happen? What is the best thing that could happen to you if you try this new skill or habit? Are these positive outcomes more likely than the negative outcomes? Compare what you wrote down for both.

DAY 56

Letting Go

"Let go of what has passed. Let go of what may come. Let go of what is happening now. Don't try to figure anything out. Don't try to make anything happen. Relax, right now, and rest."

TILOPA

There are thoughts and feelings that our minds often hold on to. However, there are other thoughts and feelings that we try to avoid or get rid of altogether.

In mindfulness practices, acceptance is often tied to an attitude of "letting go," in which we allow our experiences to be what they are without holding on to them or pushing them away. Letting go of the need to control a situation allows us the space to be patient and self-forgiving, which are foundational aspects of leading a self-compassionate life.

Daily Intention & Reflection

→ Reflect on the quote above from Tilopa, one of the most highly recognized Buddhist masters. What does "letting go" mean for you?

PART 01	PART 02	PART 03

Establishing a Self-Compassionate Lifestyle

Now that you are well versed in the fundamental practices of self-compassion, you will focus on applying them daily in order to create lasting change.

Establishing a Self-Compassionate Lifestyle - Part 01

DAY 57 | Treating Yourself Like a Close Friend

Self-kindness doesn't always come naturally to us, but practicing kindness with ourselves is more powerful than being critical with ourselves. Asking yourself, *"How would I treat a friend?"* is one of the most helpful activities for reframing self-critical thoughts.

Consider a recent situation in which you were self-critical and viewed yourself with harsh judgment. Reflect on how it made you feel. Think of a time when a friend told you about a painful or challenging experience. How did you respond to your friend?

Daily Intention & Reflection

→ How do you think you would have responded to yourself if you were going through the same experience as your friend? How does your response to your friend differ from your response to yourself?

DAY 58

Loving-Kindness

Shared humanity means recognizing that suffering, pain, and imperfection are part of being human. The better you understand shared humanity, the easier it is to treat yourself with self-compassion. The more compassionate you are with others, the more compassionate you'll be with yourself.

Showing loving-kindness to others helps you to feel more connected.[30] Practicing loving-kindness means intentionally wanting the best for others and desiring peace and happiness for them.

Daily Intention & Reflection

→   What could loving-kindness look like in your life? Why do you think loving-kindness helps develop a sense of common humanity? Next time you walk by a stranger, think to yourself, *"I wish for this person to be happy."*

DAY 59 | Self-Care - What Do I Need Right Now?

Self-care is any activity we do to take care of our mental, emotional, spiritual, or physical health. Usually, different days call for different types of self-care. What do you need right now?

Mental self-care

Make time for relaxation, learn a new skill or hobby, keep a reflective journal.

Emotional self-care

Allow your feelings to be present without judging yourself, learn to say "no," reward yourself for small tasks.

Spiritual self-care

Yoga, meditation, self-reflection, spiritual practices, mindful breathing, presence in the moment, time in nature.

Physical self-care

Go for a walk, stretch, go to bed early, give your eyes a break from screens.

Daily Intention & Reflection

→ In the space below, reflect on which areas you might want or need to practice more self-care.

→ Complete the table on the next page by providing examples of how you practice self-care in different areas of your life. For each category, list at least one specific activity or habit that you engage in regularly to take care of yourself and maintain your wellbeing.

Mental self-care	Spiritual self-care

Emotional self-care	Physical self-care

DAY 60 | # Mindfulness in the Monotonous

"The feeling that any task is a nuisance will soon disappear if it is done in mindfulness."

THICH NHAT HANH

Even the most monotonous tasks are part of living. When we do tasks like household chores, we often turn our brains off. We don't think about what we're doing in the present; our minds wander to the past, or we begin to think about the future (like when the chore might be finished).

These sorts of tasks can take up a large part of our day, meaning a large part of our day is spent not living in the moment.

Do a chore around the house such as washing the dishes or mopping the floor, and focus all of your attention on the chore itself. Do each component of the task carefully and attentively.

Daily Intention & Reflection

→   Reflect on how you felt while doing this chore. Did doing it mindfully change how you felt about it? How did you feel afterward?

DAY 61 | Deepening Gratitude

Sometimes, writing down what you are grateful for doesn't feel like enough. Thoughts of gratitude might come easily, but sometimes you need to dig deeper to truly feel gratitude.

Daily Intention & Reflection

→ In the space below, reflect on what practicing gratitude means and looks like to you.

→ Using the table on the next page, write down three things that you are grateful for today. Beside each, write down why you are grateful for these things.

I am grateful for	I am grateful for this because
01	
02	
03	

Body Scan Meditation

Find a quiet and comfortable spot, free of distractions and disruptions. Lie on your back, close your eyes, and let your breathing slow. As you breathe in and out, begin to pay attention to your breath. Feel your abdomen expand and contract. When you feel ready, begin to draw attention to other parts of your body. You might start at your feet and move to your head. You might choose a specific area of your body to pay attention to.

Acknowledge and draw your attention to any sensation you are experiencing. Do not attach judgments to these sensations; simply experience them.

Be open to these sensations and try to experience them fully. If your mind begins to wander, softly bring your attention back to your breath and then to your body. Bring your attention back with kindness and try not to be forceful.

Continue this process until you have finished scanning your entire body. Once you are finished, take a few deep and intentional breaths. Open your eyes and bring your attention back to your surroundings.

Daily Intention & Reflection

→ How did you feel coming out of this meditation?

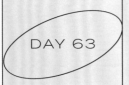

DAY 63 | Self-Compassion Reflection

Throughout this week, you've practiced self-kindness activities, gratitude reflections, and a self-care assessment. These things can help you live a life full of self-compassion.

Daily Intention & Reflection

→ Reflect on all you have learned this week. Which practice was the most helpful in allowing you to live self-compassionately? How do you feel these practices will help as you grow and develop into a more self-compassionate person?

Establishing a Self-Compassionate Lifestyle - Part 02

DAY 64

Common Humanity and Assuming the Best in Others

Has someone ever cut you off in traffic or bumped into you in line? Did you feel it ruined your day or left you feeling upset and on edge for a while afterward? We may assume that the person is a bad, inconsiderate, selfish, or impatient person.

This fuels our angst and keeps us on edge. But what if you assumed the best in the person? What if you assumed it was someone getting groceries for their sick child? What if the person was having a really tough week? Assuming the best of others helps you to feel more connected with those around you.

Daily Intention & Reflection

→ Think about the last time an interaction left you feeling upset or on edge. What if you assumed the best of the other person? How might you react differently? Think of ways you can assume the best of people in the future.

DAY 65

The Inner Advocate

We all have an inner self-critic telling us we haven't done quite enough. We rarely hear our inner advocate telling us to be proud of our accomplishments; this is the voice that stands up to the critic.

Develop your inner advocate: Reflect on your self-worth. Know that you are enough. Challenge your self-criticism.

Daily Intention & Reflection

→ On the next page, list three things about yourself that you are proud of.

→ Use the space below to reflect on what these things say about your character (e.g., kind, resilient, patient).

I am proud of

01

02

03

DAY 66 | ## What Self-Care Is and Isn't

Self-care is any activity we do to take care of our mental, emotional, spiritual, or physical health. Usually, different days call for different types of self-care.

Self-care is:

- A proactive approach to avoid becoming overwhelmed.

- A break, however big or small, from your to-do list.

- A tool to help you meet your own needs so you can live a healthy, fulfilled life.

Self-care is not:

- An emergency response plan for when you're already overwhelmed.

- Something to add to your to-do list.

- Selfish.

Daily Intention & Reflection

→ What type of self-care do you need right now?

DAY 67 | Revisiting Your Mindfulness Intention

Mindful intentions come from your heart. They are immaterial and intangible desires for self-growth. As you progress in your mindfulness practice, you learn more about yourself.

You learn about what drives you and how your thoughts shape you. Your mindfulness intention will likely evolve throughout this process of self-learning.

Daily Intention & Reflection

→ Go back to Day 16, where you first explored mindfulness. Read the intention you set for your mindfulness practice.

→ Reflect on how this intention has evolved. Has your intention changed? What have you learned since your initial mindfulness intention?

DAY 68

Gratitude for Those We Forget to Notice

When you see certain people almost every day, such as your co-workers or even the employee at the coffee shop, it can be easy to forget what they add to your life. While interactions with these people may seem small or unimportant, these people can play an important role in your life.

Write down something you are grateful for in a co-worker or someone else you interact with most days. Describe why you are grateful for them. This person shouldn't be a family member or someone you would consider a close friend. Reflect on how appreciating these small interactions helps you live with a sense of shared humanity.

Daily Intention & Reflection

→ Next time you interact with the person you wrote about, say something nice to them or let them know why you admire them.

Self-Compassion Is Not Selfish

"You yourself, as much as anybody in the entire universe, deserve your love and affection."

BUDDHA

Self-compassion is sometimes mistaken for selfishness. We think that if we're taking care of ourselves, we're not taking care of others.

When we begin to feel selfish in our self-compassion, it is important to remember the water glass metaphor; in order to pour water into another's glass, you must first have water in your own. In other words, in order to take care of others, you must first take care of yourself.

Daily Intention & Reflection

→ Since beginning this journey, what habits are you practicing which allow you to take better care of yourself?

DAY 70 | Looking Back on a Week of Self-Compassion

Each day this week, you have reflected on a different idea that will help you have a self-compassionate life.

Daily Intention & Reflection

→ What resonated with you this week? What did you connect with?

Establishing a Self-Compassionate Lifestyle - Part 03

Reframing Self-Criticism

Reframing is a helpful tool you can use any time you start to view yourself with self-judgment or criticism. It is easy to get down on ourselves when we are self-critical. Rather than being self-critical, we can work to identify when this happens and consciously reframe self-judgment to self-kindness. Recall the 4 steps to reframing below.

The 4 steps to reframing

01. Catch yourself when you are making a harsh judgment about yourself.

02. Ask yourself: *"Is the judgment completely true? Am I being overly harsh? Am I ignoring a self-compassionate response?"*

03. Think of an alternative response that is self-kind.

04. Reflect on this self-kind response. Remember this response when you find yourself making harsh self-judgments in the future.

Daily Intention & Reflection

→ Reflect on a recent instance when you were self-critical, or think of a time when you have been hard on yourself. What was your initial self-critical thought? Is this completely true? What is an alternative self-kind response? Why is this new response better?

DAY 72 — Imperfection Reflection

As humans, we all have distinct quirks that shape who we are. These quirks make us unique. Remember, you are already worthy of love.

Daily Intention & Reflection

→ Reflect on this question: What is one characteristic that makes you unique (emotionally, physically, spiritually, or mentally)?

DAY 73 | Movement as Self-Care

Physical movement is a valuable way to care for yourself. Whether it's working out, going for a walk, or stretching, movement reduces tension and stress.

What kind of movement is missing from your life lately? What do you need to do to support your body? Ask yourself these questions regularly to determine what type of self-care your body needs.

Daily Intention & Reflection

→ Write a list of movement activities you like to do. Keep this list handy and refer to it when you feel a need for physical self-care.

Accepting Struggles

"Nothing ever goes away until it has taught us what we need to know."

PEMA CHÖDRÖN

When we are experiencing a challenge in life, it can be easy to want to push the associated negative feelings away. It is often easier to distract ourselves or ignore our feelings rather than accept them. Learning how to accept our struggles can help us not only to cope with them but also to grow from them.[31]

Consider something you are struggling with right now. Write down everything you are feeling about this struggle. Start your writing with, *"Right now..."*

The next time you encounter a challenging experience, take note of how the experience made you feel. Acknowledge the physical feelings resulting from the experience, such as your breath quickening or your heart racing. During the experience, try not to push your feelings away. Instead, take a few slow, deep breaths and look for a lesson you might take from the struggle.

Daily Intention & Reflection

→ Reflect on one struggle in your life and explore any lessons you have learned from the experience.

DAY 75 | Finding Gratitude for Yourself

Feeling gratitude for yourself is just as important as feeling gratitude for others or gratitude for opportunities in your life.[32]

Write about a positive quality in yourself. Why do you think it is a positive quality? Did you learn this quality from someone else? Did someone tell you they saw this as one of your qualities? What does this positive quality bring to your life?

Daily Intention & Reflection

→   Find ways this week to express this quality through your daily actions and interactions.

DAY 76

The Journey of Self-Compassion

"To love oneself is the beginning of a lifelong romance."

OSCAR WILDE

The journey of life is a long one, and the only person guaranteed to be with you on this journey is yourself. Building a strong relationship with yourself is not always easy.

There will always be obstacles and setbacks on the road to self-compassion. However, befriending yourself is bound to bring more joy and beauty to this lifelong trip.

Daily Intention & Reflection

→ What kind of friend do you want to be for yourself?

DAY 77 | Self-Compassion Every Day

Daily affirmations can help you cultivate a healthy relationship with yourself.

Daily Intention & Reflection

→ Fill in the blanks for each of the affirmations below.

→ Challenge yourself to write or think of one affirmation every day.

I am grateful for

_____

I am proud of myself for

_____

I love myself because of the way I

_____

I am unique in my ability to

_____

I will be a _____ friend to myself.

Establishing a Self-Compassionate Lifestyle - Part 04

DAY 78 — Carving Out Time for Yourself

One of the best ways to show yourself kindness and appreciation is to carve out time for yourself. Maybe this journal has been that time for you.

As you near the end of this journal, it's important to remember to carve out some time for yourself every day to do something that brings you joy.

Daily Intention & Reflection

→ Why has this journal been important to you? Which practices will you continue to do on a daily basis?

DAY 79 | Grounding Yourself in Common Humanity

Common humanity and isolation are opposing forces. The best way to remedy feelings of isolation is to immerse yourself in feelings of common humanity.

You're not alone in this. Others understand and have gone through similar challenges. You are deserving of love because you are human.

Daily Intention & Reflection

→ What are ideas that ground you in common humanity? Are there affirmations you can tell yourself? Are there experiences that remind you of the goodness in others?

→ Create a list of things that can act as cues to remind you that you aren't in this alone and that you are fundamentally worthy of love.

DAY 80

Self-Care and Work-Life Balance

Work is one of the most commonly reported life stressors. Work can be made better or worse depending on the balance you strike between your work and your life.

What is one thing you can do to promote a healthy work-life balance? Some examples include: taking breaks, stretching your body, walking around, exercising, not responding to work emails at home, or scheduling daily priorities.

Daily Intention & Reflection

→ What is one practice you can do to promote a healthy work-life balance?

DAY 81

Missing Moments of Gratitude

Life is full of distractions, like the "busy trap" of work-life imbalance, social media feeds, or by our screens. One problem with distractions is that they prevent us from being present. If we are not present, moments of beauty in life can pass us by without notice.

We might miss the opportunity to feel gratitude or the opportunity to just experience living. Not all distractions are bad, and we don't always have to avoid them. Sometimes distractions can help us to cope or calm an overworked mind. However, consistently being distracted can take away from the present moment.

Daily Intention & Reflection

→ When do you feel most distracted or checked out? Is it when you open a social media feed or start watching a new TV show?

→ Come up with some strategies for pulling yourself away from distractions and becoming more mindful.

DAY 82

Gratitude for Where We Are

We are who we are because of where we came from, the lessons we've learned, the people we've surrounded ourselves with, and the opportunities we've been afforded.

As we move through life, we sometimes forget to stop and appreciate what we have left behind. Think about an experience in your past that has helped you in your present. Perhaps it's the town you grew up in, a childhood friend that you lost touch with, or a deep-rooted lesson that you learned from your grandparents.

Daily Intention & Reflection

→ Describe this experience from your past and consider what it brings to your present.

DAY 83

Mantra Meditation

Mindfulness meditation is about learning that we are more than our thoughts or feelings. Thoughts and feelings are fleeting, to be accepted but not held on to. Intentions can help us shape how we acknowledge these thoughts and feelings.

They can bring what we learn during our meditations into fruition in our daily lives. One way of guiding your meditation is to come up with a mantra based on your intentions. A mantra is a word or phrase you repeat to yourself to center your meditation.

Reflect on what you have learned throughout this journal about self-compassion and about yourself. Come up with a mantra based on what you've learned and how you want to grow.

A mantra can embody your intention. Your mantra does not need to be perfect, and it might change or evolve as you explore this type of meditation practice.

Your mantra can be something you have come up with on your own, or it could be a word or phrase you have found that resonates with you.

When you have chosen a mantra, find a quiet place to sit and meditate. As you meditate, repeat your mantra to yourself. Whenever your thoughts begin to wander, calmly return your attention to your mantra.

Daily Intention & Reflection

→   Why is the mantra you chose significant to you?

DAY 84 | Living a Self-Compassionate Lifestyle

Take a moment to consider the specific ways you have become more self-compassionate.

Daily Intention & Reflection

→ What practices have you begun that you can continue cultivating in your life?

WEEK 13

Bringing It All Together

DAY 85

Daily Self-Kindness

We've focused on self-kindness throughout this journal. Today, reflect on what self-kindness means to you and why it's important. What practices have been transformative for you?

Daily Intention & Reflection

→ When life gets busy, what can you do to continue to practice self-kindness? What are ways you can remind yourself to be self-compassionate?

DAY 86 | Common Humanity

Common humanity reminds us that we aren't alone in our struggles. It reminds us of the intrinsic value of others as well as of ourselves.

Daily Intention & Reflection

→ How does common humanity help you to live a self-compassionate life?

DAY 87 | A Mindful Life

Be purposeful, be present, be kind. Mindfulness helps us to become aware of our moment-to-moment experiences. It's a practice that helps us tune into our bodies, thoughts, and feelings.

Daily Intention & Reflection

→ What did you find most powerful about being mindful? What will you do to remind yourself to live in the present?

DAY 88 | Self-Acceptance

Self-acceptance focuses our attention toward our successes and positive attributes.

The more you embody your fundamental worth, the easier it becomes to accept yourself unconditionally.

Daily Intention & Reflection

→ Love yourself for who you are. What about yourself have you come to more easily accept?

DAY 89 | Gratitude

For what little things in your life do you feel gratitude? What are some things you feel grateful for that you might have taken for granted at another time? Is there anyone in your life who you want to express gratitude for?

Daily Intention & Reflection

→ Think about how you can incorporate daily thoughts of gratitude into your life. When you face challenges in the coming weeks and months, how can you remind yourself to seek gratitude?

DAY 90 | Attitude of Growth

Learning from difficult experiences provides an opportunity for growth. Patience gives you the space to forgive yourself when you don't meet your own expectations. Practicing mindfulness can help you stay in the present and avoid dwelling on the past or worrying about the future.

Whether or not you feel a big change, you've grown in many ways by completing this journal. Are you more focused on the present? Are you better at identifying when self-care is necessary?

Daily Intention & Reflection

→ Which practices do you plan to carry forward?

DAY 91 | Your Story

Take a moment to reflect on this 90-day journey you have completed. Review the letter you wrote to yourself on Day 07.

Daily Intention & Reflection

→ In what ways have you changed since writing that letter? What practices will you continue in the future?

Appendix A - Intention Setting 101

Intentions are guiding principles for how you want to be throughout your day, your week, and your life. Your intentions should be closely tied to your personal values. Intentions are not material or tangible goals you can achieve, such as buying a car or getting a promotion. Rather, intentions are visions for how your self-growth can be actualized, such as being more self-kind or being more attentive with your family. Intentions give you direction and narrow your focus, allowing for mindful personal growth.

The 5 Steps of Intention Setting

01	Identify a specific intention. The journal will help narrow your focus. The more specific you are, the more likely you will be to actualize your intention.
02	Set your intention. Writing your intention down is a powerful first step toward committing to it.
03	Commit to your intention. Tell yourself, *"This is important for me. Today, I'm going to do this."*
04	Show yourself gratitude for setting the intention. Show yourself appreciation for setting an intention that is for you and no one else.
05	Remain accountable. You may need to post a reminder, set an alarm, or write a sticky note to help you refocus on your intention, especially if it's a busy day.

Appendix B - Meditation 101

There is no right way to meditate. There are simple practices and more advanced ones. You may be experienced in meditation, or you may be a beginner. If you're a beginner, we've laid out a simple way to help you focus your attention inward to meditate. You can view this as a starting point. If something doesn't quite work, make a small tweak and show yourself appreciation for trying something new.

Meditation Using the 3 by 3 Rule

01	Find a comfortable spot. You can be sitting in a chair, sitting on the floor, or lying on your back with your arms to the side and palms open.
02	Think of an emotional need you want met.
03	Set an intention before you meditate.
04	Close your eyes. Focus on your breathing before meditating on your intention. Breathe in through your nose for 3 seconds. Hold it for 3 seconds. Breathe out through your nose for 3 seconds. Hold it for 3 seconds. Repeat.
05	Notice how the air moves through your nose and into your lungs. Notice your lungs filling from your stomach to your upper chest.
06	Whenever your mind starts to wander, gently bring your attention back to your breathing and your intention for your meditation. Accept those thoughts and move back to your meditative focus. If you begin to feel relaxed, continue to focus your mind on your intention for as long as you feel comfortable. When you are finished, take the time to slowly adjust back to your normal state.

Appendix C - Reframing Self-Critical Thoughts

Reframing is a technique where we identify the thoughts that contribute to our negative thinking and then evaluate whether these thoughts are accurate. Often, our initial reaction to a situation doesn't reflect reality. We may have an immediate self-critical thought that we believe to be true, but isn't. By reframing our thoughts, we can take the time to assess whether this self-criticism is accurate.

Steps to Reframing Self-Critical Thoughts

01	Identify when you are making a harsh judgment about yourself.
02	Ask yourself: *"Is this judgment completely true? Am I being overly harsh? Am I ignoring a self-compassionate response?"*
03	Think of an alternative response that is self-kind.
04	Reflect on the value of this self-kind response. Remember this response if you find yourself making harsh self-judgments in the future.

References

[1] Neff, K. D., & Dahm, K. A. (2015). Self-compassion: What it is, what it does, and how it relates to mindfulness. In Handbook of mindfulness and self-regulation (pp. 121-137). Springer, New York, NY.

[2] Shahar, G. (2015). Erosion: The psychopathology of self-criticism. New York: Oxford University Press.

[3] Neff, K. D. (2004). Self-compassion and psychological well-being. Constructivism in the Human Sciences, 9, 27-37.

[4] Neff, K. D. (2003). Development and validation of a scale to measure self-compassion. Self and Identity, 2, 223-250.

[5] Locke, S. R., McKay, R. C., & Jung, M. E. (2019). "I'm just too busy to exercise": Reframing the negative thoughts associated with exercise-related cognitive errors. Psychology of Sport and Exercise, 43, 279-287.

[6] Neff, K. D., & Dahm, K. A. (2015). Self-compassion: What it is, what it does, and how it relates to mindfulness. Handbook of mindfulness and self regulation (pp. 121-137). Springer, New York, NY.

[7] Neff, K. D. (2016). The self-compassion scale is a valid and theoretically coherent measure of self-compassion. Mindfulness, 7(1), 264-274.

[8] Jones, E. E., & Nisbett, R. E. (1971). The actor and the observer: Divergent perceptions of behavior. Morristown.

[9] Neff, K. D., & Dahm, K. A. (2015). Self-compassion: What it is, what it does, and how it relates to mindfulness. Handbook of mindfulness and self-regulation (pp. 121-137). Springer, New York, NY.

[10] Shapiro, S. L., Carlson, L. E., Astin, J. A., & Freedman, B. (2006). Mechanisms of mindfulness. Journal of Clinical Psychology, 62(3), 373-386.

[11] Brown, K. W., & Ryan, R. M. (2003). The benefits of being present: mindfulness and its role in psychological well-being. Journal of personality and social psychology, 84(4), 822.

[12] Chamberlain, J. M., & Haaga, D. A. (2001). Unconditional self-acceptance and psychological health. Journal of rational-emotive and cognitive-behavior therapy, 19(3), 163-176.

[13] Neff, K. (2003). Self-compassion: An alternative conceptualization of a healthy attitude toward oneself. Self and identity, 2(2), 85-101.

[14] Zhang, J. W., & Chen, S. (2016). Self-compassion promotes personal improvement from regret experiences via acceptance. Personality and social psychology bulletin, 42(2), 244-258.

[15] Algoe, S. B., Haidt, J., & Gable, S. L. (2008). Beyond reciprocity: Gratitude and relationships in everyday life. Emotion, 8(3), 425-429.

[16] Watkins, P. C. (2014). What Is Gratitude and How Can It Be Measured?. In Gratitude and the good life (pp. 13-40). Springer, Dordrecht.

[17] Rusk, R. D., Vella-Brodrick, D. A., & Waters, L. (2016). Gratitude or gratefulness? A conceptual review and proposal of the system of appreciative functioning. Journal of happiness studies, 17(5), 2191-2212.

[18] Voci, A., Veneziani, C. A., & Fuochi, G. (2019). Relating mindfulness, heartfulness, and psychological well-being: the role of self-compassion and gratitude. Mindfulness, 10(2), 339-351.

[19] Neff, K. D., & Dahm, K. A. (2015). Self-compassion: What it is, what it does, and how it relates to mindfulness. Handbook of mindfulness and self-regulation (pp. 121-137). Springer, New York, NY.

[20] Alizadeh, S., Khanahmadi, S., Vedadhir, A., & Barjasteh, S. (2018). The relationship between resilience with self-compassion, social support and sense of belonging in women with breast cancer. Asian Pacific journal of cancer prevention: APJCP,19(9) 2469.

[21] Allen, A., & Leary, M. R. (2010). Self-compassion, stress, and coping. Social and personality psychology compass, 4(2), 107-118.

[22] Breines, J. G., & Chen, S. (2012). Self-compassion increases self-improvement motivation. Personality and social psychology bulletin, 38(9), 1133-1143.

[23] "Patience." (2019). In Oxford Online Dictionary. Retrieved from https://en.oxforddictionaries.com/ definition/patience.

[24] Arch, J. J., & Craske, M. G. (2006). Mechanisms of mindfulness: Emotion regulation following a focused breathing induction. Behaviour research and therapy, 44(12), 1849-1858.

[25] Woodyatt, L., Wenzel, M., & Griffin, B. J. (Eds.). (2017). Handbook of the psychology of self-forgiveness. Springer International Publishing.

[26] Dweck, C. S. (2008). Mindset: The new psychology of success. Random House Digital, Inc.

[27] Zeidner, M., & Endler, N. S. (Eds.). (1995). Handbook of coping: Theory, research, applications (Vol.195). John Wiley &; Sons.

[28] Allen, A. B., & Leary, M. R. (2010). Self-Compassion, stress, and coping. Social and personality psychology compass, 4(2), 107-118.

[29] Drapeau, & M., Perry, J. C. (2010). The cognitive errors rating scales 3 rd edn. Unpublished manual. McGill University Montreal, Quebec author. Drapeau, M., & Perry, J. C. (2010). The Cognitive Errors Rating Scales (3rd edn)(Unpublished manual). Montreal, QC, Canada: McGill University.

[30] Hutcherson, C. A., Seppala, E. M., & Gross, J. J. (2008). Loving-kindness meditation increases social connectedness. Emotion, 8(5), 720.

[31] Shapiro, S. L., Carlson, L. E., Astin, J. A., & Freedman, B. (2006). Mechanisms of mindfulness. Journal of clinical psychology, 62(3), 373-386.

[32] Homan, K., & Hosack, L. (2019). Gratitude and the self: Amplifying the good within. Journal of Human Behavior in the Social Environment, 29(7), 874-886.